COLDPLAY

COLDPLAY
A RUSH OF BLOOD TO THE HEAD
CHORD SONGBOOK

Wise Publications
part of The Music Sales Group
London/New York/Paris/Sydney/Copenhagen/Madrid/Tokyo

Published by
Wise Publications
8/9 Frith Street, London W1D 3JB, England.

Exclusive Distributors:
Music Sales Limited
Distribution Centre, Newmarket Road, Bury St. Edmunds, Suffolk IP33 3YB, England.
Music Sales Pty Limited
120 Rothschild Avenue, Rosebery, NSW 2018, Australia.

Order No. AM977405
ISBN 1-84449-064-5
This book © Copyright 2003 by Wise Publications.

Compiled by Nick Crispin.
Music engraved by Andrew Shiels.
Printed in the United Kingdom by Caligraving Limited, Thetford, Nolfolk.

Your Guarantee of Quality
As publishers, we strive to produce every book
to the highest commercial standards.
This book has been carefully designed to minimise awkward
page turns and to make playing from it a real pleasure.
Particular care has been given to specifying acid-free,
neutral-sized paper made from pulps which have not been
elemental chlorine bleached. This pulp is from farmed sustainable
forests and was produced with special regard for the environment.
Throughout, the printing and binding have been planned to
ensure a sturdy, attractive publication which should give years
of enjoyment. If your copy fails to meet our high standards,
please inform us and we will gladly replace it.

www.musicsales.com

Amsterdam

Words & Music by Guy Berryman, Jon Buckland, Will Champion & Chris Martin

D A Esus⁴ G E Gmaj⁷ Eadd⁹ G⁶

Capo first fret

Intro

| D   A | Esus⁴ E G | D   A | Esus⁴ E G |

| D   A | Esus⁴ E G | D   A | E   G |

Verse 1

D   A   Esus⁴ E   G
Come on,   oh my   star is fading,

D   A   Esus⁴ E   G
And I   swerve out   of control.

D   A   Esus⁴ E   G
If I'd,   if I'd   only waited,

D   A   E   G
I'd not be stuck here in this   hole. __

Link 1

| D   A | Esus⁴ E G | D   A | Esus⁴ E G |

Verse 2

D   A   Esus⁴ E   G
Come here,   oh my   star is fading,

D   A   Esus⁴ E   G
And I   swerve out   of control

D   A   Esus⁴ E   G
And I   swear, I wait - ed and waited.

D   A   E   G
I've got to get out of this   hole. __

Chorus 1

Eadd⁹   Gmaj⁷
But time is on your side,

                    D   A
It's on your side   now.

              Eadd⁹
Not pushing you down,

        Gmaj⁷
And all around

              D   A
It's no cause for concern.

© Copyright 2002 BMG Music Publishing Limited.
All Rights Reserved. International Copyright Secured.

6

Instrumental 1 | D A |Esus⁴ E G |D A |Esus⁴ E G |

      |D A |Esus⁴ E G |D A |E G⁀ ‖

```
              D          A     Esus⁴ E      G
Verse 3       Come on,  oh my     star is fading,
              D      A       Esus⁴ E   G
              And I    see no chance of release.
              D      A          Esus⁴ E     G
              And I know I'm dead   on the surface
              D          A         Esus⁴ E    G
              But I am screaming under-neath. ____
```

```
                  Eadd⁹              Gmaj⁷
Chorus 2      And time is on your side,
                              D      A
              It's on your side    now.
                          Eadd⁹
              Not pushing you down,
                    Gmaj⁷
              And all around
                        D              A
              No it's no cause for concern.
```

Instrumental 2 | Eadd⁹ |Gmaj⁷ G⁶ |D |A |

      | Eadd⁹ |Gmaj⁷ G⁶ |D   A ‖

```
              A                E                      Gmaj⁷
Chorus 2        Stuck on the end   of this ball and chain
                              D          A
              And I'm on my way   back down   yeah.
                              E            Gmaj⁷
              Stood on the edge,   tied to the noose,
                            D      A
              Sick to the stomach.
                                      E
              You can say what you mean,
                                  Gmaj⁷
              But it won't change a thing
```

7

        D   **A**
I'm sick of our se - crets.

              E   **Gmaj7**
Stood on the edge,   tied to the noose

              D   **A**   **Eadd9**
And you came along,   and you cut me loose.

Gmaj7   **D**   **A**   **Eadd9**
  You came along and you cut me loose.

Gmaj7   **D**   **A**
  You came along and you cut me loose.

Animals

Words & Music by Guy Berryman, Jon Buckland, Will Champion & Chris Martin

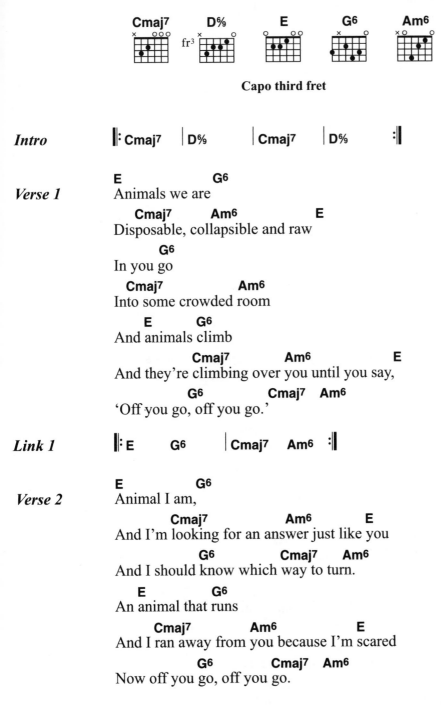

Capo third fret

Intro   ‖: Cmaj⁷ | D% | Cmaj⁷ | D% :‖

Verse 1
E   G⁶
Animals we are
　　Cmaj⁷   Am⁶   E
Disposable, collapsible and raw
　　　G⁶
In you go
　　Cmaj⁷   Am⁶
Into some crowded room
　　　E   G⁶
And animals climb
　　　　Cmaj⁷   Am⁶   E
And they're climbing over you until you say,
　　　　G⁶   Cmaj⁷ Am⁶
'Off you go, off you go.'

Link 1   ‖: E   G⁶ | Cmaj⁷   Am⁶ :‖

Verse 2
E   G⁶
Animal I am,
　　Cmaj⁷   Am⁶   E
And I'm looking for an answer just like you
　　　　G⁶   Cmaj⁷ Am⁶
And I should know which way to turn.
　　E   G⁶
An animal that runs
　　Cmaj⁷   Am⁶   E
And I ran away from you because I'm scared
　　　G⁶   Cmaj⁷ Am⁶
Now off you go, off you go.

Chorus 1

Cmaj7   **D%**
 And if you're gonna go, go now,

Cmaj7   **D%**
 And if you're gonna go, go now

Cmaj7   **D%**
 And I forgot to tell you how

Cmaj7   **D%**
 So if you're gonna go . . . go (now).

Link 2 ‖: **E** **G6** | **Cmaj7** **Am6** :‖
    now.

Verse 3

E   **G6**
Animal you are,

 Cmaj7 **Am6**
Disposable, defenceless, yes and

E   **G6**   **Cmaj7** **Am6**
 Watch your mouth boys, watch your mouth.

 E   **G6**
An animal that runs

 Cmaj7   **Am6**
And I made all my excuses to you

E   **G6**   **Cmaj7** **Am6**
 And I missed my chance by a stone's throw.

Chorus 2

Cmaj7   **D%**
 And if you're gonna go, go now,

Cmaj7   **D%**
 And if you're gonna go, go now

Cmaj7   **D%**
 And I forgot to tell you how

Cmaj7   **D%**
 So if you're gonna go . . . go . . .

             x4

Link 3 ‖: **E** **G6** | **Cmaj7** **Am6** :‖
    now.   (go)

Outro

   E   **G6**
And I crumble, crumble and fall

Cmaj7   **Am6**
Crumble and fall like an animal

 E   **G6**
I crumble, crumble and fall

Cmaj7   **Am6**
Crumble and fall like an animal

       E   **G6**
Yes I crumble, crumble and fall

Cmaj7   **Am6**
Crumble and fall like an animal

       E   **G6**
Yes I crumble, crumble and fall

Cmaj7   **Am6**
Crumble and fall like an animal.

‖: **E**   **G6** | **Cmaj7**   **Am6**   :‖

Repeat ad lib to finish

Clocks

Words & Music by Guy Berryman, Jon Buckland, Will Champion & Chris Martin

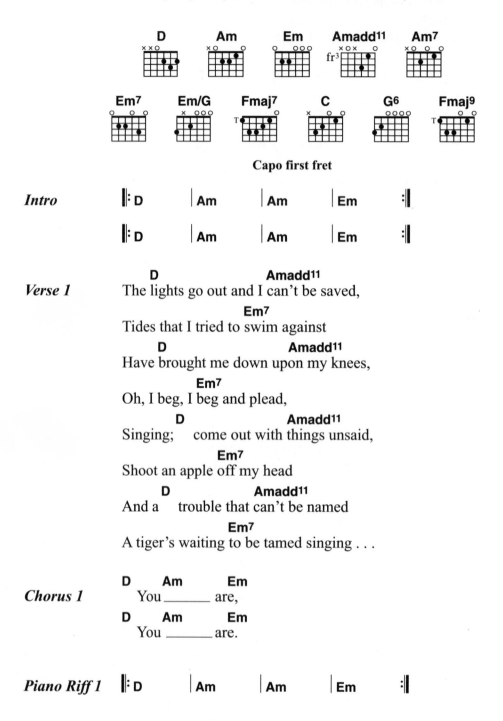

Capo first fret

Intro   ‖: D | Am | Am | Em :‖

‖: D | Am | Am | Em :‖

Verse 1

    D   Amadd¹¹
The lights go out and I can't be saved,

               Em⁷
Tides that I tried to swim against

    D   Amadd¹¹
Have brought me down upon my knees,

         Em⁷
Oh, I beg, I beg and plead,

        D   Amadd¹¹
Singing;   come out with things unsaid,

           Em⁷
Shoot an apple off my head

        D   Amadd¹¹
And a   trouble that can't be named

             Em⁷
A tiger's waiting to be tamed singing . . .

Chorus 1

D   Am   Em
  You _____ are,

D   Am   Em
  You _____ are.

Piano Riff 1 ‖: D | Am | Am | Em :‖

Verse 2

D   Amadd11
Confusion that never stops,

                   Em7
The closing walls and ticking clocks

      D   Amadd11
Gonna   come back and take you home

              Em7
I could not stop that you now know,

        D   Amadd11
Singing;   come out upon my seas,

              Em7
Cursed missed opportunities

      D   Amadd11
Am I   a part of the cure,

              Em7
Or am I part of the disease? Singing . . .

Chorus 2

D   Am   Em
  You _____ are,

D   Am   Em
  You _____ are.

D   Am   Em
  You _____ are,

D   Am   Em
  You _____ are.

Instrumental

                                                  x3

‖: D | Am7 | Am7 | Em/G   :‖

D   Am7   Em/G
  You _____ are.

Bridge

Fmaj7   C   G6
  And nothing else compares

Fmaj7   C   G6
  Oh no nothing else compares,

Fmaj7   C   G6   Fmaj7 Fmaj9 Fmaj7 Fmaj9
  And nothing else compares.

Piano riff 2

‖: D | Am | Am | Em   :‖

‖: D | Am7 | Am7 | Em/G   :‖

Chorus 3

D   Am7   Em/G
You ———— are,

D   Am7   Em/G
You ———— are.

Outro

‖:
D   Am7   Em/G
Home, home, where I wanted to go.

D   Am7   Em/G
Home, home, where I wanted to go. :‖

Repeat to fade

Crests Of Waves

Words & Music by Guy Berryman, Jon Buckland, Will Champion & Chris Martin

B7sus4   C#m   F#m7   G#m7   B   A   G#7

Intro

| B7sus4 | |

| C#m | F#m7 G#m7 | C#m | F#m7 G#m7 |

| C#m | F#m7 G#m7 | F#m7 | G#m7 B |

Verse 1

           C#m   A
It could be worse, I could be alone
         F#m7   G#m7
I could be locked in here on my own
           C#m   A
Or like a stone that certainly drops
         F#m7 G#m7
It never stops, no.
  B   C#m   A
I could be lost, or I could be saved
        F#m7   G#m7
Calling out from beneath the waves
       C#m   A
Beaten down by the sloshing rain
     F#m7   G#m7   B
Never again, never again.

Chorus 1

C#m   F#m7   G#m7
Oo - oo - oo
C#m   F#m7   G#m7
Oo - oo - oo
C#m   F#m7   G#m7
Oo - oo - oo
     F#m7   G#m7
Skating out from the crests of waves.

Link 1

| C#m | F#m7 G#m7 | C#m | F#m7 G#m7 |

| C#m | F#m7 G#m7 | F#m7 | G#m7 B |

Verse 2

     C♯m   **A**
   It could be worse, it's all sweet

      F♯m7   **G♯m7**
   You could be snapped from the jaws of defeat.

     C♯m7   **A**
   Or like a light lit up on a beach

          F♯m7 **G♯m7**
   Wear your heart on your sleeve, oh.

   B   **C♯m**   **A**
   You want to stop before you begin

      F♯m7   **G♯m7**
   You want to sink when you know you could swim.

     C♯m   **A**
   You want to stop just before you begin

     F♯m7   **G♯m7** **B**
   Never give in, never give in.

Chorus 2

C♯m   **F♯m7** **G♯m7**
Oo - oo - oo

C♯m   **F♯m7** **G♯m7**
Oo - oo - oo

C♯m   **F♯m7** **G♯m7**
Oo - oo - oo

    F♯m7   **G♯m7**
Skating out from the crests of waves.

Bridge

 A
  Nothing matters,

F♯m7 **G♯m7**
  Except life and the love we make

 A
  Nothing matters

F♯m7 **G♯m7**
  Except life and the love we make

 A
  Nothing matters

F♯m7 **G♯m7**
  Except life and the love we make

F♯m7 **G♯m7**
      Except life and the love we make.

Chorus 3

C#m   F#m⁷   G#m⁷
Oo - oo - oo

C#m   F#m⁷   G#m⁷
Oo - oo - oo

C#m   F#m⁷   G#m⁷
Oo - oo - oo

      F#m⁷   G#m⁷
Skating out from the crests of waves.

C#m   F#m⁷   G#m⁷
Oo - oo - oo

C#m   F#m⁷   G#m⁷
Oo - oo - oo

C#m   F#m⁷   G#m⁷
Oo - oo - oo

      F#m⁷   G#m⁷
Skating out from the crests of waves.

      F#m⁷   G#m⁷
You're longing to be saved,

      F#m⁷   G#m⁷
Screaming out from the crests of waves,

      F#m⁷   G#m⁷
You're longing to be saved,

      F#m⁷   G#m⁷
Screaming out from the crests of waves.

Daylight

Words & Music by Guy Berryman, Jon Buckland, Will Champion & Chris Martin

F#5   E6   Gmaj7(♭5)   Amaj7   Dmaj7   F#

Intro

‖: F#5 | F#5 | F#5 | F#5 :‖

‖: E6 | Gmaj7(♭5) F#5 | F#5 | F#5 :‖

Verse 1

      E6 Gmaj7(♭5) F#5
To my sur - prise

       E6 Gmaj7(♭5) F#5
And my de - light.

      E6 Gmaj7(♭5)   F#5
I saw sun   rise

      E6 Gmaj7(♭5) F#5
I saw sun - light.

Verse 2

     E6 Gmaj7(♭5) F#5
I am no - thing

      E6 Gmaj7(♭5) F#5
In the dark.

       E6   Gmaj7(♭5) F#5
And the clouds   burst

      E6 Gmaj7(♭5)   F#5
To show day - light.

Chorus 1

Amaj7   Dmaj7
Ooh, — and the sun will shine

F#   Amaj7
Yeah, __ on this heart of mine.

        Dmaj7
Ooh,— and I realise

F#   Amaj7
Who, __ cannot live without

      Dmaj7   (F#5)
Ooh, — come apart without, yeah.

Link 1

| F#5 | F#5 | F#5 | F#5 | |

‖: E6 | Gmaj7(♭5) F#5 | F#5 :‖

Verse 3

      E6 Gmaj7(♭5) F#5
On a hill   -   top

      E6 Gmaj7(♭5) F#5
On a sky   rise.

        E6   Gmaj7(♭5) F#5 E6   Gmaj7(♭5) F#5
Like a first   born child.

Verse 4

      E6 Gmaj7(♭5) F#5
On a full   tilt,

        E6   Gmaj7(♭5) F#5
And in full   flight

        E6   Gmaj7(♭5) F#5
Defeat dark   -   ness

          E6 Gmaj7(♭5) F#5
Breaking day   -   light.

Chorus 2

Amaj7   Dmaj7
Ooh, ___ and the sun will shine

F#   Amaj7
Yeah, ___ on this heart of mine.

               Dmaj7
Ooh,___ and I realise

F#   Amaj7
Who, ___ cannot live without

Amaj7   Dmaj7   F#5 | F#5 | F#5 | F#5 ‖
Ooh, ___ come apart without, daylight.

Outro

   E6   Gmaj7(♭5)
‖: Slowly breaking through   the daylight,

F#5
Slowly breaking through the daylight. :‖   *Repeat to fade*

19

God Put A Smile Upon Your Face

Words & Music by Guy Berryman, Jon Buckland, Will Champion & Chris Martin

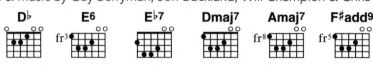

Tune down one and a half tones

Intro | D♭ | E6 | E♭7 | E♭7 Dmaj7 |

| D♭ | E6 | E♭7 | Dmaj7 ‖

Verse 1
D♭   E6   E♭7   Dmaj7
Where do we go, nobody knows!
D♭   E6   E♭7   Dmaj7
I've gotta say I'm on my way ___ down.
D♭   E6   E♭7   Dmaj7
God give me style and give me grace.
D♭   E6   E♭7   Dmaj7
God put a smile upon my face. _____

Guitar Solo 1 | D♭ | E6 | E♭7 | E♭7 Dmaj7 |

| D♭ | E6 | E♭7 | Dmaj7 ‖

Verse 2
D♭   E6   E♭7   Dmaj7
Where do we go to draw the line?
D♭   E6   E♭7   Dmaj7
I've gotta say I've wasted all your time, honey, honey
D♭   E6   E♭7   Dmaj7
Where do I go to fall from grace?
D♭   E6   E♭7   Dmaj7
God put a smile upon your face. Yeah.

Chorus 1
Amaj7   E6   F♯add9   Amaj7
And ah _____ when you work it out I'm worse than you. _____
E6   F♯add9   Amaj7
Yeah, _____ when you work it out I wanted to. _____
E6   F♯add9   Amaj7
And ah _____ when you work out where to draw the line, _____
E6 F♯add9
Your guess is as good as mine.

Guitar Solo 2 | D♭ | E6 | E♭7 | E♭7   Dmaj7 |

                | D♭ | E6 | E♭7 | Dmaj7   ‖

Verse 3

   D♭   E6   E♭7   Dmaj7
    Where do we go nobody knows

   D♭   E6   E♭7   Dmaj7
    Don't ever say you're on your way down

       D♭   E6   E♭7   Dmaj7
  When God gave you style and gave you grace,

   D♭   E6   E♭7   Dmaj7
    And put a smile upon your face, oh yeah.

Chorus 2

       Amaj7   E6   F♯add9   Amaj7
  And ah, when you work it out I'm worse than you. _____

                 E6   F♯add9   Amaj7
  Yeah, when you work it out I wanted to. _____

                 E6   F♯add9   Amaj7
  And ah, when you work out where to draw the line, _____

                E6   F♯add9   D♭   E6   E♭7
  Your guess is as good as mine. _____

       Dmaj7   D♭   E6   E♭7
  It's as good as mine. _____

       Dmaj7   D♭   E6   E♭7
  It's as good as mine. _____

       Dmaj7   D♭   E6
  It's as good as mine. _____

  E♭7
  Na na na na na na na na na na

       Dmaj7   Amaj7   E6
  It's as good as mine. _____

  F♯add9   Amaj7   E6
  It's as good as mine. _____

  F♯add9   Amaj7   E6   F♯add9
  It's as good as mine. _____

Outro

   D♭   E6   E♭7   Dmaj7
    Where do we go nobody knows

   D♭   E6   E♭7   Dmaj7
    Don't ever say you're on your way down

       D♭   E6   E♭7   Dmaj7
  When God gave you style and gave you grace

   D♭   E6   E♭7   Dmaj7
    And put a smile upon your face.

21

Green Eyes

Words & Music by Guy Berryman, Jon Buckland, Will Champion & Chris Martin

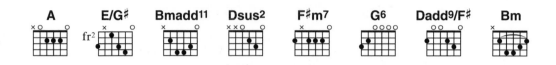

Verse 1

    A   E/G♯   Bmadd11
Honey you   are a rock,

    A   E/G♯   Bmadd11
Upon which I stand.

    A   E/G♯   Bmadd11
And I come here to talk,

    A   E/G♯   Bmadd11
I hope you understand.

Verse 2

    Bmadd11
That Green Eyes,

        Dsus2
Yeah the spot light

        A   E/G♯
Shines upon you.

    Bmadd11   Dsus2
And how could anybody,

    A   E/G♯ F♯m7
Deny you?

Chorus 1

Bmadd11   Dsus2
  I came here with a load,

           A G6   Dadd9/F♯
And it feels so much light - er now I met you.

Bmadd11   Dsus2
  And honey you should know,

         A G6   Dsus2
That I could never go on   without you.

Bmadd11 | Bmadd11 | Bmadd11 | Bmadd11 ‖
Green Eyes.

Verse 3

```
    A              E/G♯        Bmadd11
     Honey you    are the sea,
    A    E/G♯          Bmadd11
    Upon which I float.
    A         E/G♯           Bmadd11
     And I came here to talk
    A         E/G♯          Bmadd11
     I think you should know.
```

Verse 4

```
          Bmadd11
    That Green Eyes,
             Dsus2               A       E/G♯
    You're the one that I wanted to find.
          Bmadd11
    And any one who
          Dsus2
    Tried to deny you
                      A            E/G♯  F♯m7
    Must be out of their minds.
```

Chorus 2

```
    Bmadd11                      Dsus2
     Because I came here with a load,
                         A  G6       Dadd9/F♯
    And it feels so much light - er since I met you.
    Bmadd11                 Dsus2
     ι And honey you should know,
                      A    G6      Dsus2
    That I could never go on    without you.
    Bm
    Green Eyes,

    Green Eyes,
          A
    Oh oh oh.
             Bm
    Oh oh oh.

    Oh oh oh.
```

Outro

```
    A              E/G♯        Bmadd11
     Honey you    are a rock
    A     E/G♯        Bmadd11
    Upon which I stand.
```

23

I Bloom Blaum

Words & Music by Guy Berryman, Jon Buckland, Will Champion & Chris Martin

D(#11)　　Dadd9　　D　　Gm(add11)

A　　Asus2/4　　A*　　B7　　D*

Tune guitar

⑥ = D   ③ = F#
⑤ = A   ② = A
④ = D   ① = D

Intro

| D(#11) | Dadd9　D(#11) | D(#11) | Dadd9　D(#11) |

| D(#11) | Dadd9　D(#11) | D(#11) | Dadd9　D(#11) |

| D | D | D(#11) | Dadd9　D(#11) |

| D(#11) | Dadd9　D(#11) | Gm(add11) | Gm(add11) ‖

Verse

Gm(add11)　　　　　　　D(#11)
Darling, those tired eyes

Gm(add11)　　　　　　　　D(#11)
　Go with me all the time.

Gm(add11)　　　　　　　　D(#11)
　And in the dead of night

Gm(add11)　　　　　　　D(#11)
　Tell me you will be mine.

A　　　　　Asus2/4　A*　　　Asus2/4
Where do you go to,　　pretty baby?

A　　　　　Asus2/4　　　A*　　　　Asus2/4
Where do you go to, when the night wins away.

A　　　　　Asus2/4　A*　　　Asus2/4
　Ask me so sweetly,　what do I do?

A　　　　Asus2/4
　Who do I sing for?

　　A*　　Asus2/4　　B7　　　　Gm(add11)　　　　D(#11)
Well honey I sing about you. _____

B7　　　Gm(add11)　　D(#11)　　　　D
You. _____

I Ran Away

Words & Music by Guy Berryman, Jon Buckland, Will Champion & Chris Martin

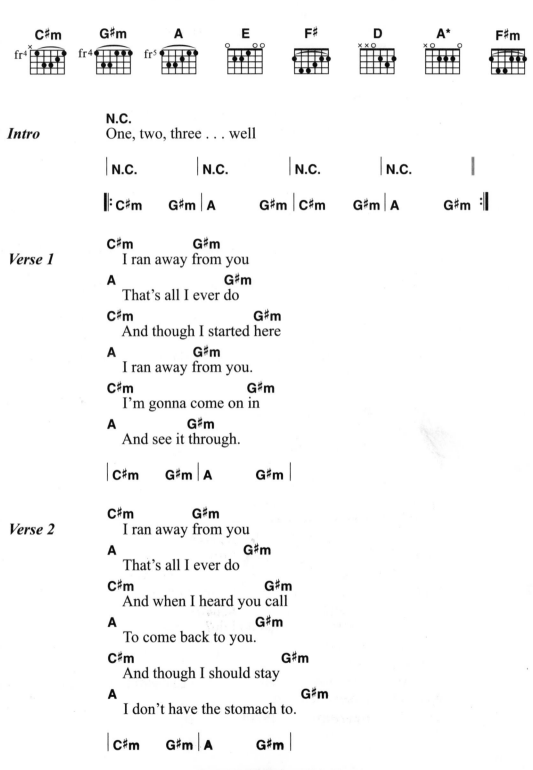

Intro

N.C.
One, two, three . . . well

| N.C. | N.C. | N.C. | N.C. |

‖: C#m   G#m | A   G#m | C#m   G#m | A   G#m :‖

Verse 1

C#m   G#m
  I ran away from you

A   G#m
  That's all I ever do

C#m   G#m
  And though I started here

A   G#m
  I ran away from you.

C#m   G#m
  I'm gonna come on in

A   G#m
  And see it through.

| C#m   G#m | A   G#m |

Verse 2

C#m   G#m
  I ran away from you

A   G#m
  That's all I ever do

C#m   G#m
  And when I heard you call

A   G#m
  To come back to you.

C#m   G#m
  And though I should stay

A   G#m
  I don't have the stomach to.

| C#m   G#m | A   G#m |

Chorus 1

    E   F♯
Everyone I know,

            D   A*
Says I'm a fool to mess with you,

    E   F♯
Everyone I know

            D   A*
Says it's a stupid thing to do.

    E   F♯
I have your love on call

            D   A*
And yet my day was so full

                D   A*
There might be nothing left to do

      D   A*
So I ran away from you.

Link   ‖: C♯m   G♯m | A   G♯m | C♯m   G♯m | A   G♯m :‖

Verse 3

  C♯m   G♯m
I'm gonna come on in

  A   G♯m
My eyes are closed.

  C♯m   G♯m
I can feel it there

  A   G♯m
The sun's so close.

  C♯m   G♯m
I'm gonna come on out

  A   G♯m
And burn the sky.

| C♯m   G♯m | A   G♯m |

Verse 4

  C♯m   G♯m
A star arose,

  A   G♯m
In my own cage

  C♯m   G♯m
I'm stuck in line

  A   G♯m
And in a cage

  C♯m   G♯m
Just a single star

  A   G♯m
I see it fall.

cont. | C♯m   G♯m | A   G♯m |

          E   F♯
Chorus 2   Everyone I know,
                   D   A*
        Says I'm a fool to mess with you,
          E   F♯
         Everyone I know
                 D   A*
       Says it's a stupid thing to do.
          E   F♯
        I have your love on call
                 D   A*
       And yet my day was so full
                  D   A*
       There might be nothing left to do
          D   A*
       So I ran away from you.

                       x7
Outro ||: C♯m | F♯m   :|| C♯m | A |
                                                      x3
            ||: E | F♯ | D | A   :||
             | D | A | D | A ||

In My Place

Words & Music by Guy Berryman, Jon Buckland, Will Champion & Chris Martin

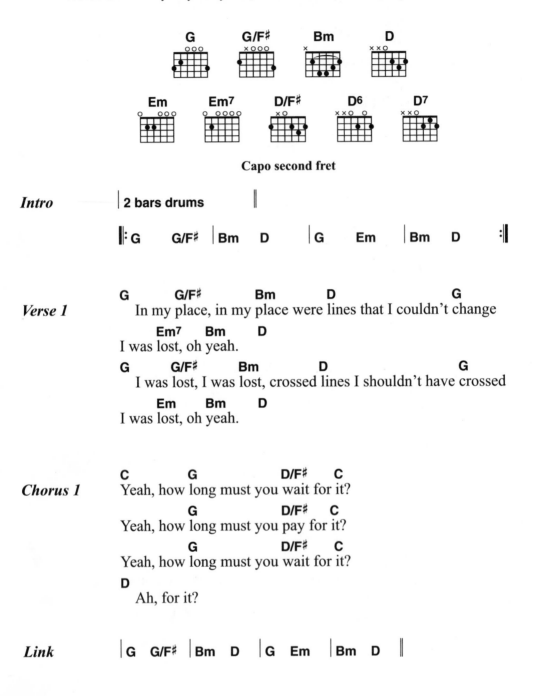

Capo second fret

Intro ‖ 2 bars drums ‖

‖: G   G/F♯ | Bm   D | G   Em | Bm   D :‖

Verse 1

G G/F♯ Bm   D   G
  In my place, in my place were lines that I couldn't change
  Em7 Bm D
I was lost, oh yeah.
G G/F♯ Bm   D   G
  I was lost, I was lost, crossed lines I shouldn't have crossed
  Em Bm   D
I was lost, oh yeah.

Chorus 1

C   G   D/F♯ C
Yeah, how long must you wait for it?
    G   D/F♯ C
Yeah, how long must you pay for it?
    G   D/F♯ C
Yeah, how long must you wait for it?
D
  Ah, for it?

Link | G G/F♯ | Bm D | G Em | Bm D ‖

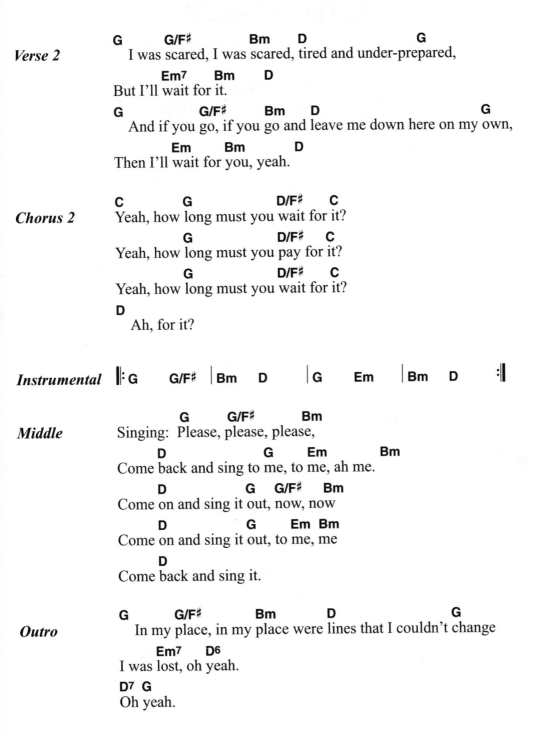

Verse 2

G   G/F♯   Bm   D   G
    I was scared, I was scared, tired and under-prepared,

    Em7   Bm   D
But I'll wait for it.

G   G/F♯   Bm   D   G
    And if you go, if you go and leave me down here on my own,

    Em   Bm   D
Then I'll wait for you, yeah.

Chorus 2

C   G   D/F♯   C
Yeah, how long must you wait for it?

    G   D/F♯   C
Yeah, how long must you pay for it?

    G   D/F♯   C
Yeah, how long must you wait for it?

D
    Ah, for it?

Instrumental ‖: G   G/F♯ | Bm   D | G   Em | Bm   D   :‖

Middle

    G   G/F♯   Bm
Singing: Please, please, please,

    D   G   Em   Bm
Come back and sing to me, to me, ah me.

    D   G   G/F♯   Bm
Come on and sing it out, now, now

    D   G   Em Bm
Come on and sing it out, to me, me

    D
Come back and sing it.

Outro

G   G/F♯   Bm   D   G
    In my place, in my place were lines that I couldn't change

    Em7   D6
I was lost, oh yeah.

D7 G
Oh yeah.

One I Love

Words & Music by Guy Berryman, Jon Buckland, Will Champion & Chris Martin

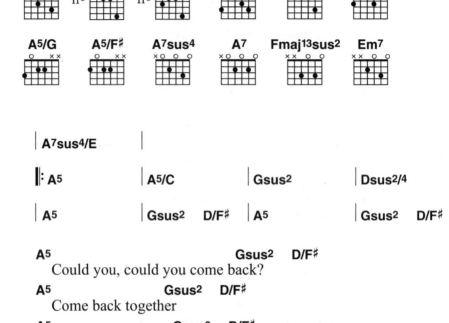

Intro

| A7sus4/E |

‖: A5 | A5/C | Gsus2 | Dsus2/4 :‖ *x4*

| A5 | Gsus2 D/F♯ | A5 | Gsus2 D/F♯ ‖

Verse 1

A5   Gsus2   D/F♯
   Could you, could you come back?

A5   Gsus2   D/F♯
Come back together

A5   Gsus2   D/F♯
  Put yourself on the band

A5   Gsus2   D/F♯
And see us forever.

A5   Gsus2   D/F♯
  Could you, could you come home?

A5   Gsus2   D/F♯
Come home forever,

A5   Gsus2   D/F♯
  Surely things in the band

A5   Gsus2   D/F♯
Keep us together.

Chorus 1

| A5 | A5/C | Gsus2 | Dsus2/4 |
                         'Cause you're the one I love

| A5 | A5/C | Gsus2 | Dsus2/4 |
                        You're the one I love

| A5 | A5/C | Gsus2 | Dsus2/4 |
                        You're the one I love

| A5 | A5/C | Gsus2 | Dsus2/4 |
  Ah,   ah.

	x2

Link 1   ‖: **A5**　　　| **A5/C**　　　| **Gsus2**　　　| **Dsus2/4**　　　:‖

Verse 2

A5　　　　　　　　　**Gsus2**　　**D/F♯**
Could you, could you come in?

A5　　　　　　　　**Gsus2**　　**D/F♯**
Could you tell me wherever?

A5　　　　　　**Gsus2**　　**D/F♯**
Tie yourself to a mast

A5　　　　　　**Gsus2**　　**D/F♯**
It's now or it's never.

A5　　　　　　**Gsus2**　　**D/F♯**
Could it tear us apart?

A5　　　　　　**Gsus2**　　**D/F♯**
It'll soon be forever

A5　　　　　　**Gsus2**　　**D/F♯**
It's gonna tear us apart

A5　　　　**Gsus2**　　**D/F♯**
Keep us together.

Chorus 2

| **A5**　　| **A5/C**　　| **Gsus2**　　| **Dsus2/4**　　|
You're the one I love

| **A5**　　| **A5/C**　　| **Gsus2**　　| **Dsus2/4**　　|
You're the one I love

| **A5**　　| **A5/C**　　| **Gsus2**　　| **Dsus2/4**　　|
Ah.　　　　　Ah.　　　　　You're the one I love

| **A5**　　| **A5/C**　　| **Gsus2**　　| **Dsus2/4**　　|
The one I love.

Link 2   ‖: **A5**　| **A5**　　| **A5**　　| **A5**　　:‖
Ooooooooooo

| **A5**　| **A5**　| **A5/G**　| **A5/F♯**　　|
Ooooooooooo.

	x4

Outro   ‖: **A5**　　　| **A5/C**　　　| **Gsus2**　　　| **Dsus2/4**　　　:‖

x2

‖: **A7sus4**　　| **A7sus4**　　| **A7**　　| **A7**　　:‖

x3

‖: **Fmaj13sus2**　　| **Em7**　　| **A7**　　| **A7**　　:‖

| **Fmaj13sus2**　　| **Em7**　　| **A7**　　‖

1.36

Words & Music by Guy Berryman, Jon Buckland, Will Champion & Chris Martin

E5/G   E5   G6   F#6add11   B7   B7sus4

Capo first fret

Intro | E5/G   E5 | E5/G   E5 |

| E5/G   E5 | E5/G   E5   ‖

E5/G   E5
Verse 1   Stuck in a corner

E5/G   E5
Are mon - keys in cages

E5/G   E5
That don't have a number

E5/G   E5
To fight one another.

G6   F#6add11
Try to recover.

| E5/G   E5 | E5/G   E5 |

E5/G   E5
Climb up the ladder

E5/G   E5
Look up   and you see birds

E5/G   E5
Blind as each other.

E5/G   E5
How long can we suffer?

G6   F#6add11
We're as blind as each other.

| E5/G   E5 | E5/G   E5 |

| E5/G   E5 | E5/G   E5 |

Chorus 1

B⁷   **B⁷sus⁴**
On the cloud that you sit in

B⁷   **B⁷sus⁴**
There's one born every minute

B⁷ **B⁷sus⁴**
So much to discover,

B⁷   **B⁷sus⁴**
I've become a believer.

| **E⁵/G** **E⁵** | | **E⁵/G** **E⁵** | | |

| **E⁵/G** **E⁵** | | **E⁵/G** **E⁵** | | |

Verse 2

E⁵/G **E⁵**
Sis - ters and brothers,

    E⁵/G E⁵
Who fight one another

    E⁵/G **E⁵**
Will mourn and deceive us,

    E⁵/G E⁵
Will find us and keep us.

G⁶ **F♯6add11**
Take us or leave us.

| **E⁵/G** **E⁵** | | **E⁵/G** **E⁵** | | |

E⁵/G E⁵
How soon is now? Yeah.

E⁵/G E⁵
How long is never?

    E⁵/G E⁵
I'm no - thing but normal

    E⁵/G **E⁵**
With some - thing together.

G⁶   **F♯6add11**
Come on, stick together.

| **E⁵/G** **E⁵** | | **E⁵/G** **E⁵** | | |

| **E⁵/G** **E⁵** | | **E⁵/G** **E⁵** | | |

Chorus 2

B7　　　　**B7sus4**
　On the cloud that you sit in

B7　　　　　**B7sus4**
　There's one born every minute

B7　**B7sus4**
　So much to discover,

B7　　　**B7sus4**
　I've become a believer.

Outro　　| **E5/G**　**E5**　　　　　| **E5/G**　**E5**　　　　　|

　　　　　　| **E5/G**　**E5**　　　　　| **E5/G**　**E5**　　　　　|

　　　　　　| **E5/G**　**E5**　　　　　| **E5/G**　**E5**　　　　　|

　　　　　　| **E5/G**　**E5**　　　　　| **E5/G**　**E5**　　　　　|

　　　　　　| **G6**　　　　　　　　| **F♯6add11**　**N.C.**　‖

A Rush Of Blood To The Head

Words & Music by Guy Berryman, Jon Buckland, Will Champion & Chris Martin

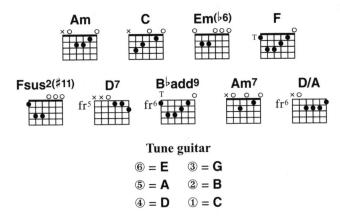

Tune guitar

⑥ = E   ③ = G
⑤ = A   ② = B
④ = D   ① = C

Verse 1

      Am   **C**
He said I'm gonna buy this place and burn it down,
  Em(♭6)   **Am**
I'm gonna put it six feet underground.

He said I'm gonna buy this place and watch it **C** fall
  Em(♭6)   **Am**
Stand here beside me baby in the crumbling walls.

Verse 2

     Am   **C**
Oh I'm gonna buy this place and start a fire,
  Em(♭6)   **Am**
Stand here until I fill all your heart's desires.

Because I'm gonna buy this place and see it **C** burn
  Em(♭6)   **Am** |**Am** |
Do back the things it did to you in return.

Link 1

  F   **Fsus2(♯11)**
Ha _ ha _____
  F   **Fsus2(♯11)**
Ha _ ha._____

Verse 3

                Am   **C**
He said I'm gonna buy a gun and start a war,
  Em($\flat$6)   **Am**
If you can tell me something worth fighting for.

Oh and I'm gonna buy this place, is what I say,   **C**
Em($\flat$6)   **Am** | **Am** |
Blame it upon a rush of blood to the head.

Chorus 1

         F   **D7**
Honey, all the movements you're starting to make

                                  F
See me crumble and fall on my face.

                             D7
And I know the mistakes that I've made,
      B$\flat$add9   **F**
See it all disappear without a trace,

                            D7
And they call as they beckon you on,
        B$\flat$add9   **(Am)**
They said start as you mean to go on.

| **Am** | **C** | **Em($\flat$6)** |

Am
  Start as you mean to go on.

| **Am** | **C** | **Em($\flat$6)** | **Am** |

Verse 4

                Am   **C**
He said I'm gonna buy this place and see it go,
  Em($\flat$6)   **Am**
Stand here beside my baby, watch the orange glow.

                              C
Some will laugh and some just sit and cry,
  Em($\flat$6)   **Am**
But you just sit down there and you wonder why.

Verse 5

              Am   **C**
So I'm gonna buy a gun and start a war,
Em($\flat$6)   **Am**
If you can tell me something worth fighting for.

                                 C
Oh and I'm gonna buy this place, is what I say,
Em($\flat$6)   **Am**
Blame it upon a rush of blood to the head, oh to the head.

Chorus 2

    F   **D7**

Honey, all the movements you're starting to make

                                     F

See me crumble and fall on my face.

                                  D7

And I know the mistakes that I've made,

    B♭add9   **F**

See it all disappear without a trace,

                              D7

And they call as they beckon you on,

        B♭add9   **(Am)**

They said start as you mean to go on.

Am   **C**   **Em(♭6)**

    As you mean to go on,

Am

   As you mean to go on.

| **Am** | **C** | **Em(♭6)** | |

Verse 6

Am

  So meet me by the bridge,

                 C

Oh meet me by the lake.

              Em(♭6)   **Am**

When am I gonna see that pretty face again?

Oh meet me on the road,

                C

Oh meet me where I ____ said,

       Em(♭6)   **Am7**   **D/A**

Blame it all upon a rush of blood to the head.

Outro | **Am7** **D/A** | **Am7** **D/A** | **Am7** **D/A** | **Am** | ‖

Politik

Words & Music by Guy Berryman, Jon Buckland, Will Champion & Chris Martin

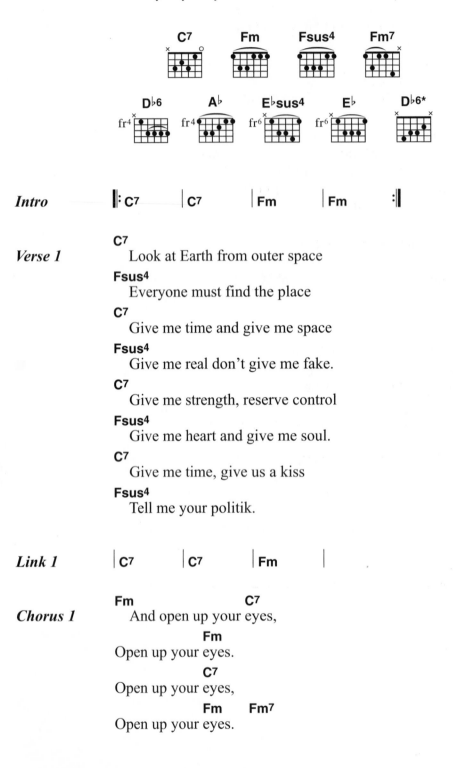

Intro ‖: C7 | C7 | Fm | Fm :‖

Verse 1

C7
Look at Earth from outer space

Fsus4
Everyone must find the place

C7
Give me time and give me space

Fsus4
Give me real don't give me fake.

C7
Give me strength, reserve control

Fsus4
Give me heart and give me soul.

C7
Give me time, give us a kiss

Fsus4
Tell me your politik.

Link 1 | C7 | C7 | Fm |

Chorus 1

Fm   C7
And open up your eyes,

Fm
Open up your eyes.

C7
Open up your eyes,

Fm   Fm7
Open up your eyes.

Verse 2

C7
Give me one, 'cause one is best,

Fsus4
In confusion confidence

C7
Give me peace of mind, and trust

Fsus4
And don't forget the rest of us.

C7
Give me strength, reserve control

Fsus4
Give me heart and give me soul.

C7
Wounds that heal, and cracks that fix

Fsus4
Tell me your politik.

Chorus 2

           C7
And open up your eyes,

       Fm
Open up your eyes.

       C7
Open up your eyes,

       Fm
Open up your eyes.

  Fm7   C7
Just open up your (eyes.)

Link 2

| C7 | C7 | Fm | Fm | D♭6 | |

eyes.

| D♭6 | A♭ | A♭ | E♭sus4 | E♭ | ‖

Outro

Fm   D♭6*   A♭ E♭sus4 E♭ Fm
Give me love over, love over, love over this. Ah._____

                 D♭6*   A♭   E♭sus4 E♭
Give me love over, love over, love over this. Ah, ah _____

| Fm | Fm | D♭6* | D♭6* | A♭ | A♭ | |

| E♭sus4 | E♭ | Fm | Fm | D♭6* | D♭6* | |

| A♭ | A♭ | E♭sus4 | E♭ | Fm | ‖

39

The Scientist

Words & Music by Guy Berryman, Jon Buckland, Will Champion & Chris Martin

Intro   ‖: Dm7 | Bb | F | Fsus2   :‖

Verse 1

Dm7   Bb
    Come up to meet you,

          F
Tell you I'm sorry,

                     Fsus2
You don't know how lovely you are.

Dm7   Bb
  I had to find you,

         F
Tell you I need you,

            Fsus2   C/F
Tell you I'll set   you apart.

Dm7   Bb
   Tell me your secrets,

                F
And ask me your questions,

            Fsus2   C/F
Oh let's go back to the start.

Dm7   Bb
   Running in circles,

         F
Coming up tails,

            Fsus2   C/F
Heads on a silence apart.

Chorus 1

Bb
   Nobody said it was easy,

F   Fsus2
   It's such a shame for us to part.

Bb
   Nobody said it was easy,

cont.

F   C/F   Fsus2   C
No-one ever said it would be this hard.

C/G   (F)
Oh, take me back to the start.

Link | F | B♭ | F | F | F | B♭ | F | Fsus2 ‖

Verse 2

Dm7   B♭
I was just guessing

             F
At numbers and figures,

          Fsus2
Pulling your puzzles apart.

Dm7   B♭
Questions of science,

            F
Science and progress,

           Fsus2
Do not speak as loud   as my heart.

Dm7   B♭
Tell me you love me,

           F
Come back and haunt me,

        Fsus2
Oh and I rush to the start.

Dm7   B♭
Running in circles,

           F
Chasing our tails,

        Fsus2
Coming back as we are.

Chorus 2

B♭
Nobody said it was easy,

F   Fsus2
Oh it's such a shame for us to part.

B♭
Nobody said it was easy,

F   C/F   Fsus2   C
No-one ever said it would be so hard.

C/G   (F)
I'm going back to the start.

Instrumental | F | B♭ | F | F | Dm7 | B♭ | F | F   ‖

Outro

Dm7	B♭	F	F	

Dm7   B♭   F | F |
Ooh _____

Dm7   B♭   F | F |
Ah ooh _____

Dm7   B♭   F | F |
Oh ooh _____

Dm7   B♭   ⌢F
Oh ooh.

42

Warning Sign

Words & Music by Guy Berryman, Jon Buckland, Will Champion & Chris Martin

Dadd⁹   G   D   A   E   Esus⁴

F#m   Em/G   E/G#   Gmaj7   F#m7   Em7/A   Dmaj7/F#

Capo first fret

Intro

| Dadd⁹ | Dadd⁹ | Dadd⁹ | Dadd⁹ |

‖: G   D | A   E | G   D | A   E :‖

Verse 1

    G   D
A warning sign,

  A   Esus⁴ E   G   D
   I missed the good part then I realised,

  A   Esus⁴ E   G   D
   I started looking and the bubble burst,

  A   Esus⁴ E   G   D   A   Esus⁴
   I started looking for excuses.

Verse 2

    G   D
Come on in,

  A   Esus⁴ E   G   D
   I've got to tell you what a state I'm in.

  A   Esus⁴ E   G   D
   I've got to tell you in my loudest tones

  A   Esus⁴   E   G   D
   That I started looking for a warning sign.

| A   Esus⁴   E | E |

Chorus 1

           D   F#m
When the truth is

        A   E/G#
I miss you.

          D   F#m
Yeah, the truth is

          A   E/G#
That I miss you so.

Guitar solo |G   D |A Esus⁴ E |G   D |A Esus⁴ E |

Guitar solo |G   D |A Esus4 E |G   D |A Esus4 E |

            G   D
Verse 3   A warning sign

            A   Esus⁴   E
            You came back to haunt me

                G   D
            And I realised,

            A   Esus⁴ E
            That you were an island

               G   D
            And I passed you by,

            A   Esus⁴ E   G   D
            When you were an island to discover.

          |A   Esus⁴   E |

            G   D
Verse 4   Come on in,

            A   Esus⁴ E   G   D
            I've got to tell you what a state I'm in.

            A   Esus⁴ E   G   D
            I've got to tell you in my loudest tones

            A   Esus⁴   E   G   D
            That I started looking for a warning sign.

          |A   Esus⁴   E |E |

                 D   F♯m
Chorus 2   When the truth is

               A   E/G♯
            I miss you.

                D   F♯m
            Yeah, the truth is

                 A   E/G♯
            That I miss you so.

              Gmaj⁷ F♯m⁷
            And I'm tired,

                      A   E/G♯ |E/G♯ |
            I should not have let you go.

Middle | A | Em7/A | G | Dmaj7/F♯ |
Oh.

| A | Em7/A | G | Dmaj7/F♯ |

Outro

     A   Em7/A   G   Dmaj7/F♯
So I crawl back into your open arms.

     A   Em7/A   G   Dmaj7/F♯
Yes I crawl back into your open arms.

     A   Em7/A   G   Dmaj7/F♯
And I crawl back into your open arms.

     A   Em7/A   F♯m
Yes I crawl back into your open arms.

A Whisper

Words & Music by Guy Berryman, Jon Buckland, Will Champion & Chris Martin

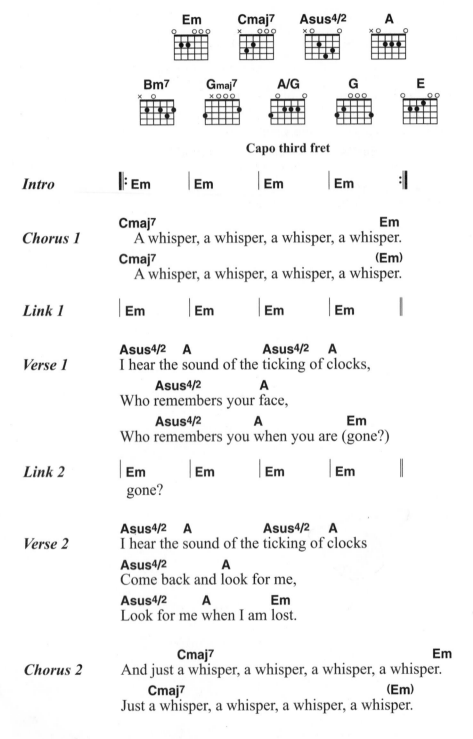

Em   Cmaj7   Asus4/2   A

Bm7   Gmaj7   A/G   G   E

Capo third fret

Intro ‖: Em | Em | Em | Em :‖

Chorus 1
Cmaj7   Em
  A whisper, a whisper, a whisper, a whisper.
Cmaj7   (Em)
  A whisper, a whisper, a whisper, a whisper.

Link 1 | Em | Em | Em | Em ‖

Verse 1
Asus4/2   A   Asus4/2   A
I hear the sound of the ticking of clocks,
   Asus4/2   A
Who remembers your face,
   Asus4/2   A   Em
Who remembers you when you are (gone?)

Link 2 | Em | Em | Em | Em ‖
  gone?

Verse 2
Asus4/2   A   Asus4/2   A
I hear the sound of the ticking of clocks
Asus4/2   A
Come back and look for me,
Asus4/2   A   Em
Look for me when I am lost.

Chorus 2
      Cmaj7   Em
And just a whisper, a whisper, a whisper, a whisper.
   Cmaj7   (Em)
Just a whisper, a whisper, a whisper, a whisper.

| *Link 3* | Em | Em | Em | Em ‖ |

Middle

Bm⁷   Cmaj⁷   A
Night turns to day, and I still have these questions,
Bm⁷   Cmaj⁷   A
Bridges will break, should I go forwards or backwards?
       Bm⁷   Cmaj⁷   A   A/G
And night turns to day, and I still get no answers.

| Em | Em | |

Chorus 3

Cmaj⁷   Em
      A whisper, a whisper, a whisper, a whisper.
       Cmaj⁷   Em
Just a whisper, a whisper, a whisper, a whisper.

| *Link 4* | Em | Em | Em | |

Verse 3

Asus⁴/² A   Asus⁴/² A
I hear the sound of the ticking of clocks,
       Asus⁴/²   A
Who remembers your face,
       Asus⁴/²   A   Em | Em |
Who remembers you when you are gone?

Verse 4

Asus⁴/² A   Asus⁴/² A
I hear the sound of the ticking of clocks
Asus⁴/²   A
Come back and look for me,
Asus⁴/²   A   Em
Look for me when I am lost.

Chorus 4

       Cmaj⁷   Em
And just a whisper, a whisper, a whisper, a whisper.
       Cmaj⁷
Just a whisper, a whisper, a whisper, a whisper.

| *Link 4* | E | E | E | E ‖ |

Outro

‖: G   A | E | G   A | E |
| G   A | E | G   A | E :‖ *Repeat to fade*

47

Relative Tuning

The guitar can be tuned with the aid of pitch pipes or dedicated electronic guitar tuners which are available through your local music dealer. If you do not have a tuning device, you can use relative tuning. Estimate the pitch of the 6th string as near as possible to E or at least a comfortable pitch (not too high, as you might break other strings in tuning up). Then, while checking the various positions on the diagram, place a finger from your left hand on the:

5th fret of the E or 6th string and **tune the open A** (or 5th string) to the note Ⓐ

5th fret of the A or 5th string and **tune the open D** (or 4th string) to the note Ⓓ

5th fret of the D or 4th string and **tune the open G** (or 3rd string) to the note Ⓖ

4th fret of the G or 3rd string and **tune the open B** (or 2nd string) to the note Ⓑ

5th fret of the B or 2nd string and **tune the open E** (or 1st string) to the note Ⓔ

E **A** **D** **G** **B** **E**
or or or or or or
6th 5th 4th 3rd 2nd 1st

Head

Nut

1st Fret

2nd Fret

3rd Fret

4th Fret

5th Fret

Reading Chord Boxes

Chord boxes are diagrams of the guitar neck viewed head upwards, face on as illustrated. The top horizontal line is the nut, unless a higher fret number is indicated, the others are the frets.

The vertical lines are the strings, starting from E (or 6th) on the left to E (or 1st) on the right.

The black dots indicate where to place your fingers.

Strings marked with an O are played open, not fretted. Strings marked with an X should not be played.

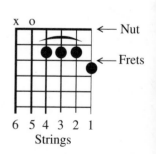

The curved bracket indicates a 'barre' – hold down the strings under the bracket with your first finger, using your other fingers to fret the remaining notes.